Flute Book 1

PREMIER PERFORMANCE®

AN INNOVATIVE AND COMPREHENSIVE BAND METHOD

by Ed Sueta

Dear Band Student:

*Welcome to **Premier Performance!** Congratulations on your decision to learn to play the flute. Learning to play the flute will be a rewarding and satisfying experience. You will develop an appreciation for music which will be a source of enjoyment throughout your life.*

*By playing in the band, you will make new friends and have a great deal of fun performing for your family, classmates and community. Your band director, a good instrument, a desire to learn and **Premier Performance®** will be all you need to begin your journey into the exciting world of instrumental music. With regular practice, you will quickly develop the musical skills necessary to become an outstanding musician.*

Best wishes for musical success!

Ed Sueta

Instruments provided courtesy
of **The Selmer Company, Inc.**

Special thanks to Fine Arts Supervisor **Richard Haas** and the
students and teachers of the **Bloomfield Public Schools** for
their participation in the photographs on pages 2 and 3.

PUTTING YOUR FLUTE TOGETHER

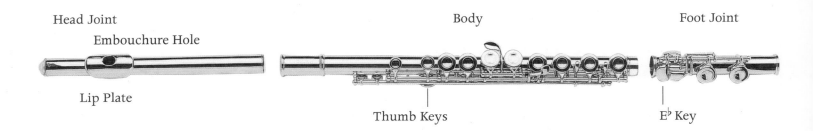

Head Joint

Embouchure Hole

Lip Plate

Body

Thumb Keys

Foot Joint

E♭ Key

STEP ONE

♦ Hold the head joint in your hand without touching the lip plate. In your other hand, grasp the top of the body.

♦ Using a gentle twisting motion, insert the head joint into the body. Turn the two parts in opposite directions until the center of the embouchure hole is in line with the keys of the body.

STEP TWO

♦ Hold the foot joint away from the keys and twist it on to the body.

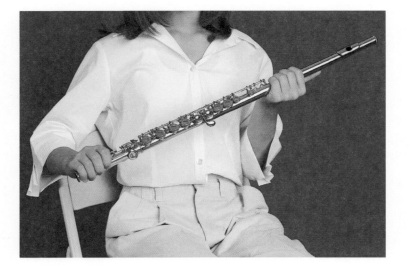

STEP THREE

♦ Rotate the foot joint until the key rod is in line with the center of the bottom key of the body.

♦ Remember: Never hold the flute by the keys or key rods.

FLUTE CARE

♦ When you are finished playing, take apart your instrument.

♦ Wrap a soft, clean cloth over the cleaning rod. Dry each section by inserting the cloth.

♦ To keep your flute looking good, gently wipe the keys with a separate, soft, clean cloth.

♦ Place all the parts of your flute in your case and latch it.

POSTURE AND PLAYING POSITION

♦ Sit up straight on the front part of your chair.
♦ Keep your head up, feet flat on the floor and look straight ahead.
♦ Relax your shoulders and move them down and back a little.
♦ Place your left thumb on the thumb key farthest to the right. Bring your fingers around the flute. Keep them slightly arched with the pads of your fingers slightly above the center of the keys.
♦ Place your right thumb below and on the inner side of the flute under the F key. Do not allow your thumb to extend beyond the body of the flute. Place your right hand pinky on the E♭ key.
♦ Curve the left hand under the flute for support and balance. Push forward with the right thumb into the left index finger with firm pressure.
♦ Tilt your head slightly to the right with your elbows away from your body.

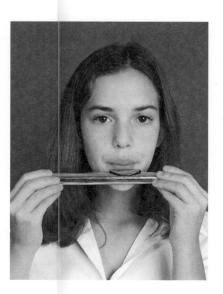

EMBOUCHURE

Producing a beautiful tone is one of your main goals when playing the flute. The French word embouchure (ahm' buh sure) describes the formation of your lips and mouth. Your embouchure and the air you breathe into the flute will determine the quality of your tone.

♦ At first, practice only with the head joint. Hold the head joint with both hands with the open end to the right.
♦ Rest the lip plate firmly into the crook of the chin slightly below the edge of the lower lip, making sure the tube is parallel to your lips. The center of the embouchure hole should be at the center of your lips.
♦ Hold the corners of your lips firm to your teeth. You are now ready to play your first tone.

PLAYING YOUR FIRST TONE

♦ Form your embouchure.
♦ Take a deep breath through the corners of your mouth. Keep your shoulders steady.
♦ Make your lip opening as small as possible.
♦ Release your breath by whispering a firm "Too." Direct the air across the opposite edge of the embouchure hole. Your lower lip will partly cover the hole.
♦ Hold the tone for several seconds.
♦ Always take deep breaths and use a firm air stream.
♦ Repeat these steps several times.
♦ Repeat these steps with your flute assembled.

PREMIER PROGRESS PRACTICE CHART

DATE	ASSIGNMENT/FOCUS POINTS	M	T	W	T	F	S	S	TOTAL	PARENT SIGNATURE

QUARTERLY GRADE _____

DATE	ASSIGNMENT/FOCUS POINTS	M	T	W	T	F	S	S	TOTAL	PARENT SIGNATURE

QUARTERLY GRADE _____

DATE	ASSIGNMENT/FOCUS POINTS	M	T	W	T	F	S	S	TOTAL	PARENT SIGNATURE

QUARTERLY GRADE _____

DATE	ASSIGNMENT/FOCUS POINTS	M	T	W	T	F	S	S	TOTAL	PARENT SIGNATURE

QUARTERLY GRADE _____

FINAL GRADE _____

READING MUSIC

Music Staff	Treble Clef	Bar Line

The music staff consists of 5 lines and 4 spaces.	A treble clef sign is placed at the beginning of a music staff and indicates the position of the G. The G is on the second line of the staff.	A bar line is a vertical line which divides the staff into measures.

Measure		Double Bar
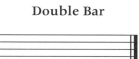		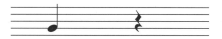
A measure is the distance between two bar lines.		A double bar line marks the end of the music.

TIME SIGNATURES

4/4 = 4 beats in a measure
4/4 = quarter note receives 1 beat

3/4 = 3 beats in a measure
3/4 = quarter note receives 1 beat

2/4 = 2 beats in a measure
2/4 = quarter note receives 1 beat

Whole note Whole rest	Half note Half rest	Quarter note Quarter rest
A whole note and whole rest each receive 4 beats in 4/4 time.	A half note and half rest each receive 2 beats in 4/4 time.	A quarter note and quarter rest each receive 1 beat in 4/4 time.

NAMES OF NOTES

Line Notes	Space Notes
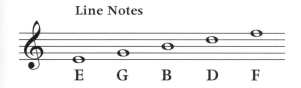	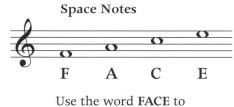
E G B D F	F A C E
Memorize this sentence to remember the line notes: Every Girl (and) Boy Does Fine.	Use the word **FACE** to remember the space notes.

C D E F G A B C D E F G A B C D E F

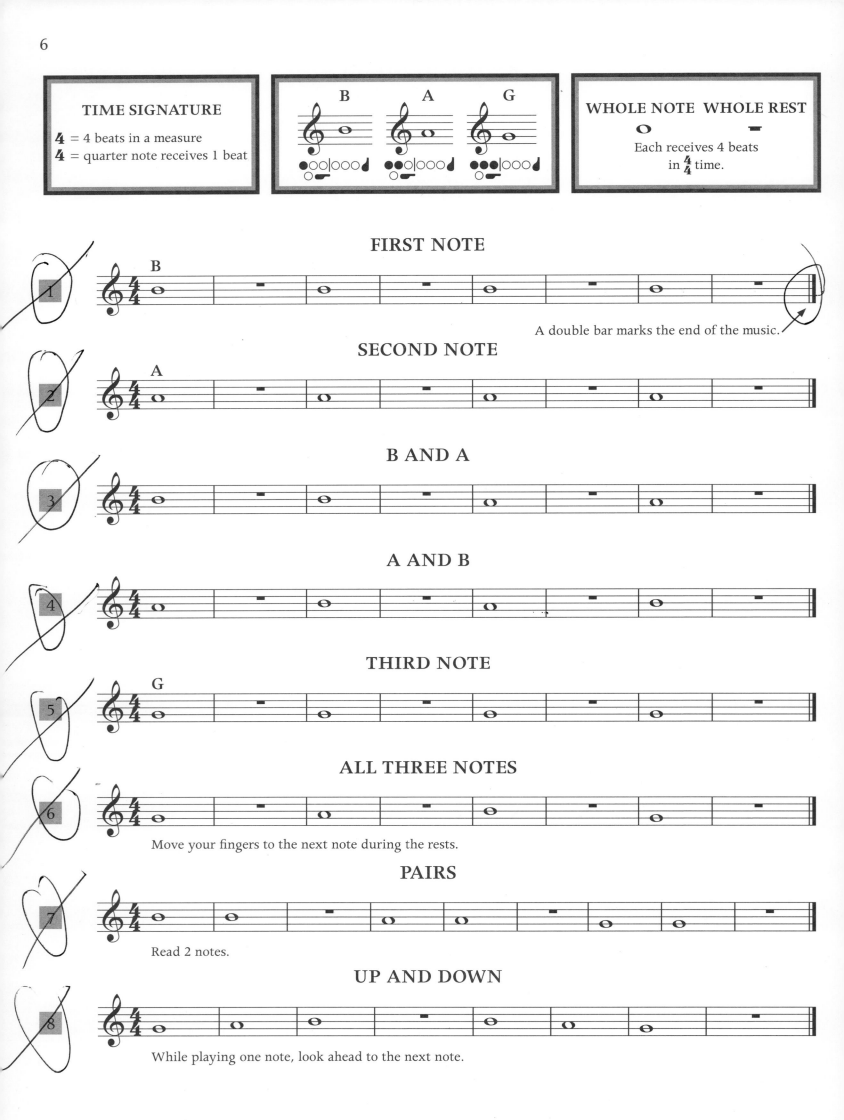

2 TAPS

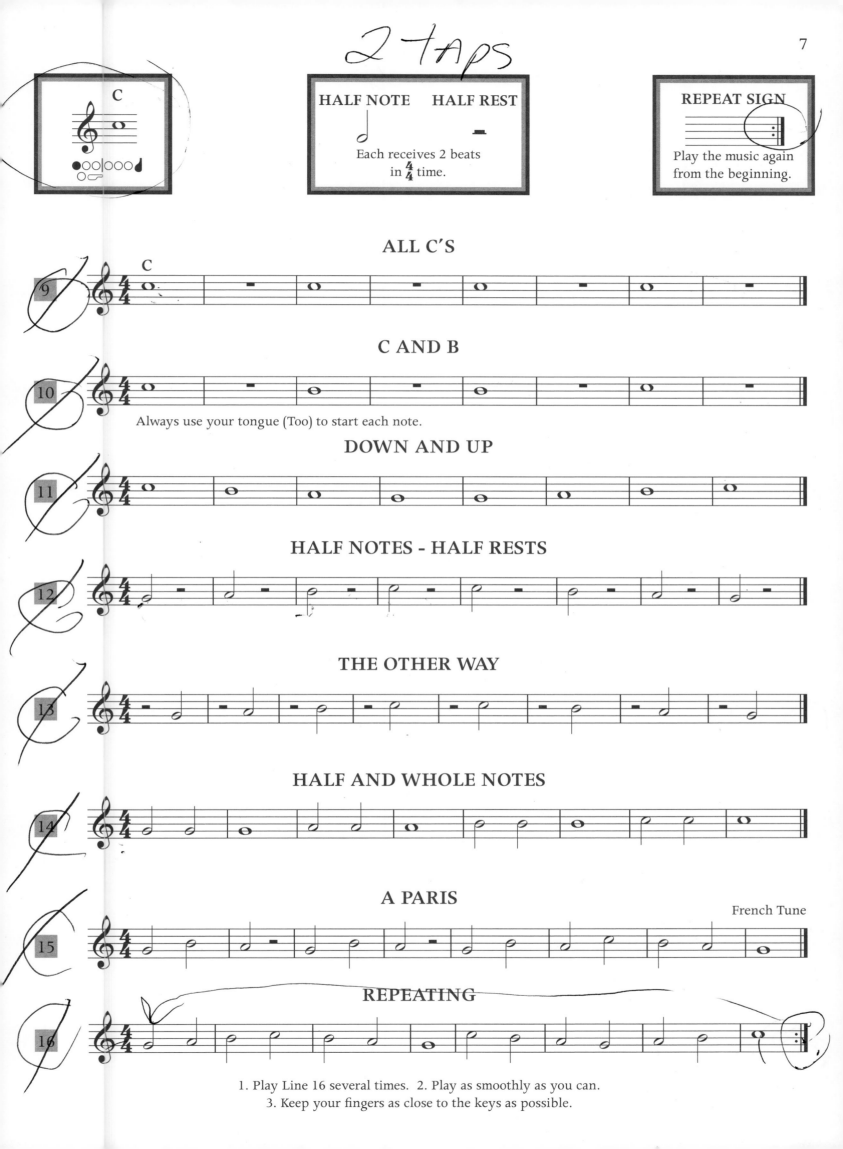

HALF NOTE   HALF REST

Each receives 2 beats
in $\frac{4}{4}$ time.

REPEAT SIGN

Play the music again
from the beginning.

ALL C'S

C AND B

Always use your tongue (Too) to start each note.

DOWN AND UP

HALF NOTES - HALF RESTS

THE OTHER WAY

HALF AND WHOLE NOTES

A PARIS

French Tune

REPEATING

1. Play Line 16 several times. 2. Play as smoothly as you can.
3. Keep your fingers as close to the keys as possible.

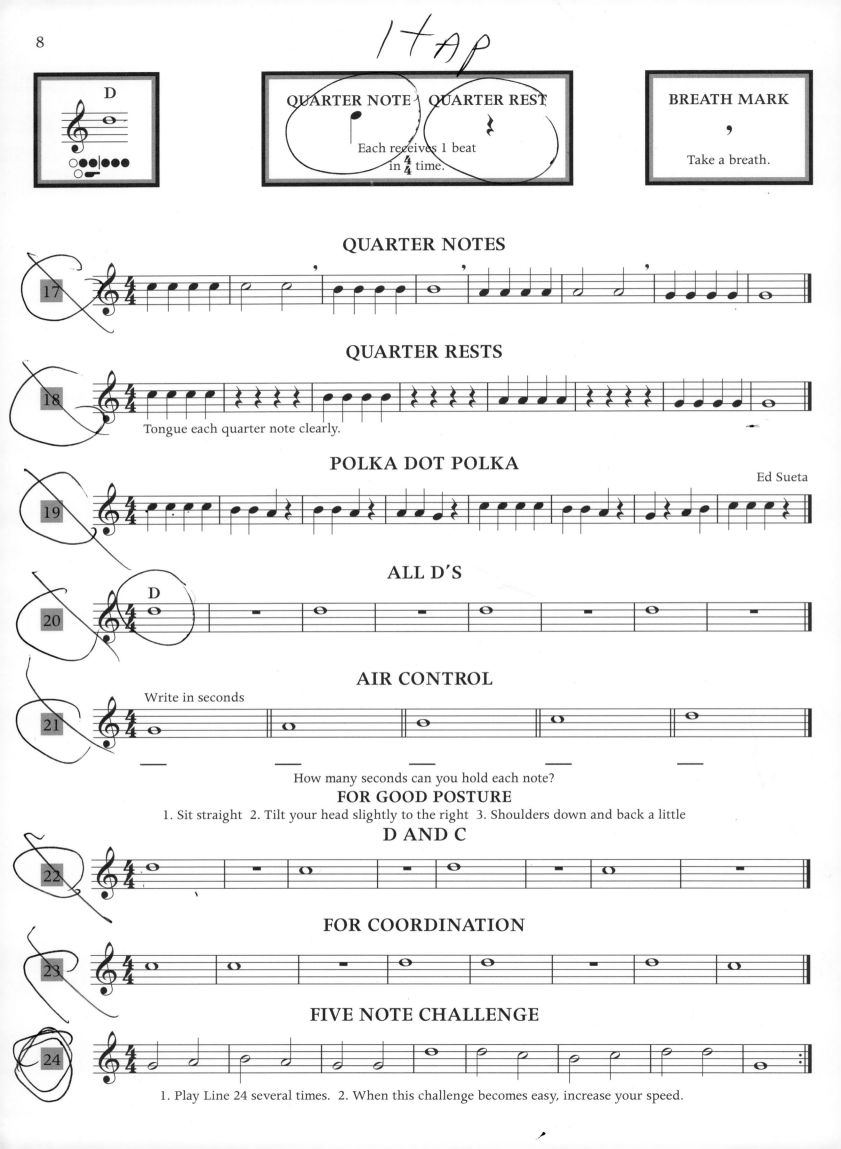

GOOD KING WENCESLAS

Traditional

INDIAN CHANT

Native American

Slowly

Add the bar lines and then play Indian Chant.

ROCKIN'

Ed Sueta

TEAMWORK - DUET

Ed Sueta

JINGLE BELLS

James S. Pierpont
(1822-1893)

FOR SMOOTH PLAYING

Finger and say the notes before you play this line. Be sure to tongue each note clearly.

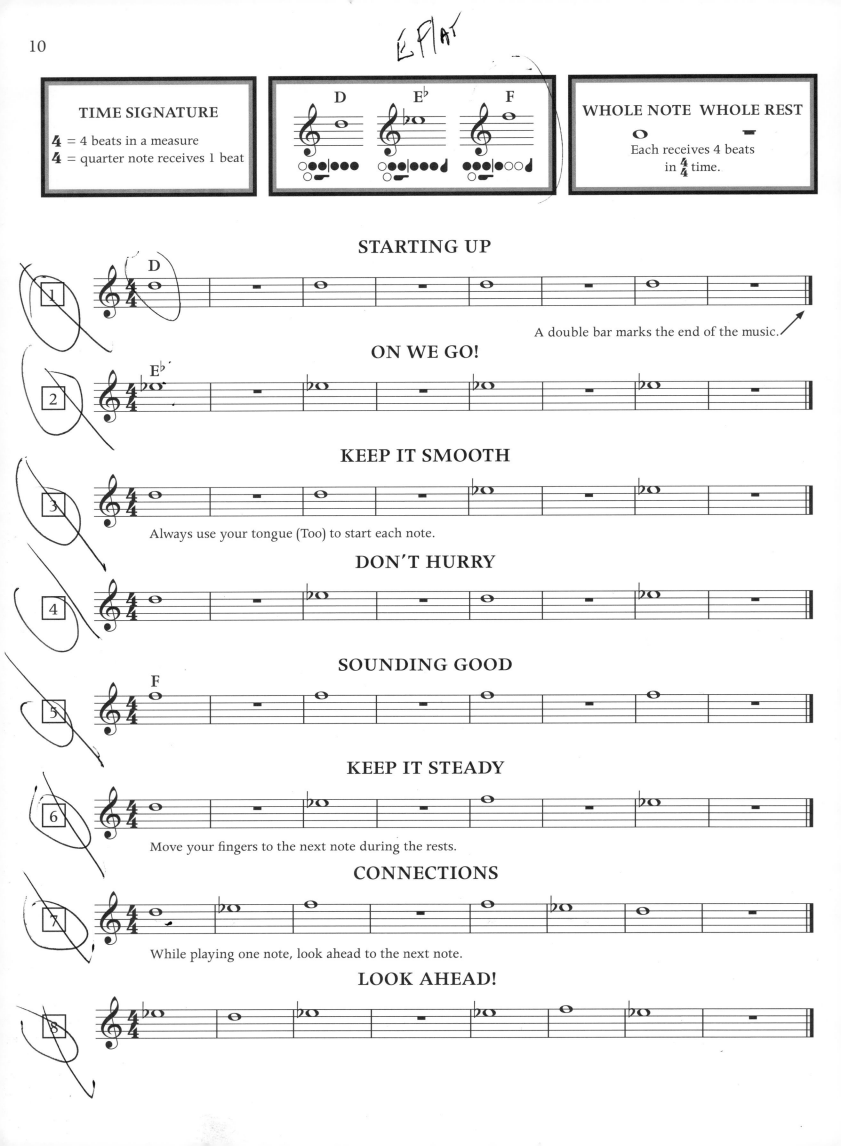

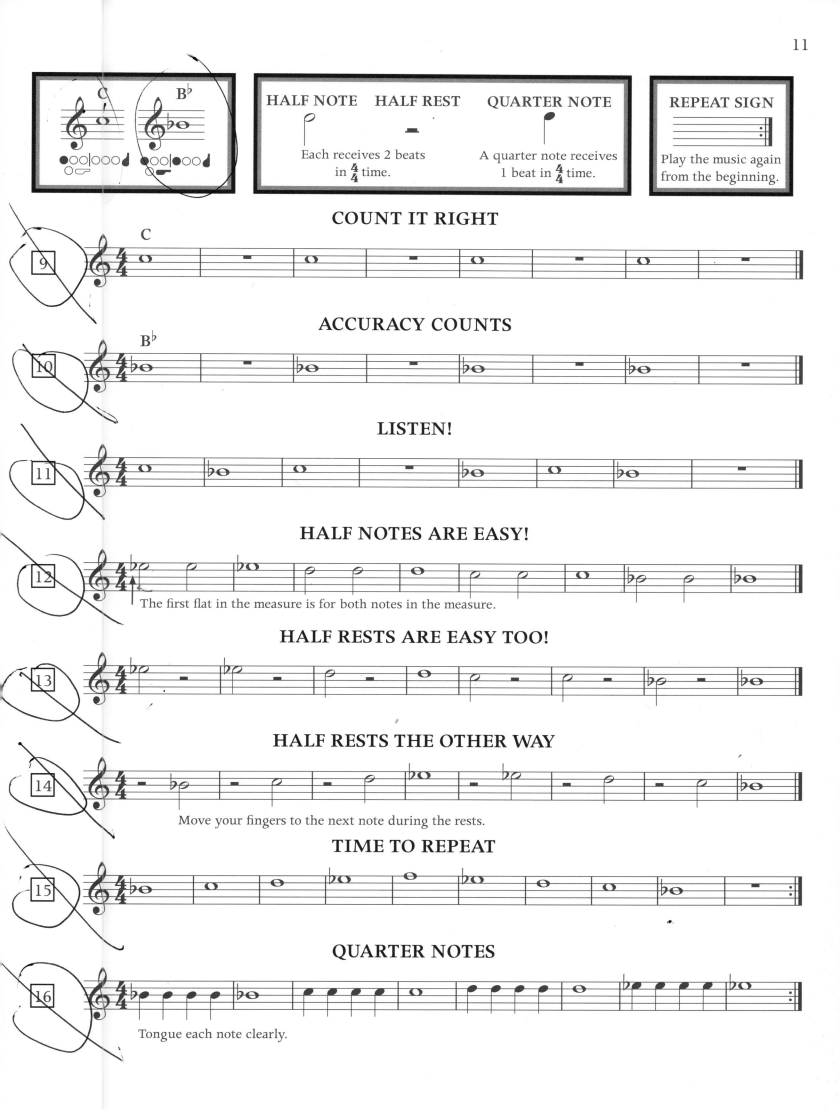

RHYTHM PATTERNS

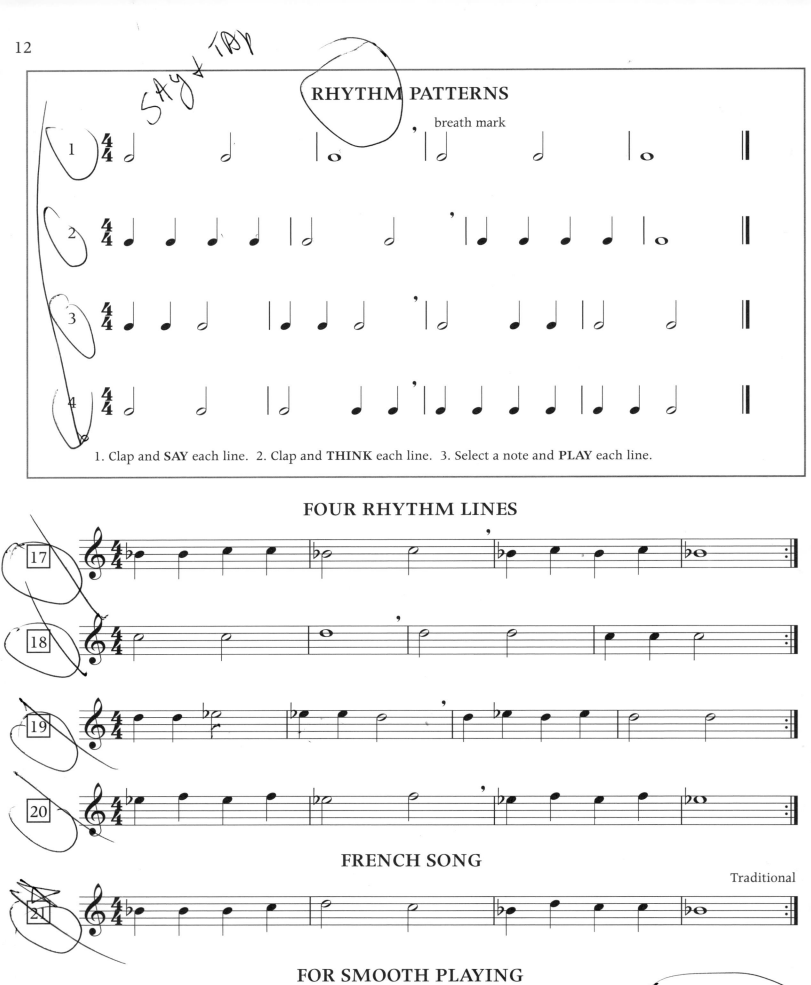

breath mark

1. Clap and **SAY** each line. 2. Clap and **THINK** each line. 3. Select a note and **PLAY** each line.

FOUR RHYTHM LINES

FRENCH SONG

Traditional

FOR SMOOTH PLAYING

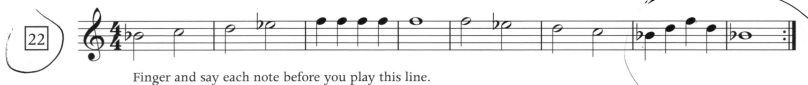

Finger and say each note before you play this line.

TIME SIGNATURE	1st & 2nd ENDINGS	ROUND	TIE
2 = 2 beats in a measure **4** = quarter note receives 1 beat	Play the 1st ending and repeat from the beginning. Skip the 1st ending and play the 2nd ending.	Playing the same music but beginning at different times	A tie is a curved line that connects 2 or more notes of the same pitch. Tongue the first note only.

MARCH PRIMO

Ed Sueta

23

MERRILY WE ROLL ALONG

Game Song

24

1. (1st ending)   2. (2nd ending)

2nd time

TWO PART ROUND

English

25

The first player starts at the beginning. When the first player reaches ②, the second player starts at the beginning.

FRENCH TUNE

Traditional

26

AIR CONTROL

27

FOR COORDINATION

28

RHYTHM COMPOSITION

Complete the measures below. Use quarter notes, half notes and whole notes.

29

When you have finished, clap your composition. Make any changes you feel are necessary.

Play Premier Technique Lines 1 and 2 on page 44.

14

A

KEY SIGNATURE

Indicates which notes are flatted or sharped. Your first key signature has two flats - B♭ and E♭.

∦

Repeat the previous measure.

DIVISI

Some players play the upper notes. Other players play the lower notes.

SMOOTH ALL THE WAY

30

Key signature

HARMONY

31A

I - Tonic Chord   V - Dominant Chord   I   I   V   I

Your teacher will explain the chord symbols.

31B

31C

JINGLE BELLS DUET

James S. Pierpont
(1822-1893)

32A

32B

V   I

divisi

TIME TO COMPOSE _____   Composer _____
                                    [TITLE]   [Your Name]

33

Use the Rhythm Composition you created in Line 29 and add notes to compose your own melody.
1. Start and end on B♭. 2. Use only the notes that you have learned. 3. Name your composition. 4. Play your composition.

Play Premier Technique Lines 3 and 4 on page 44.

Play Premier Rhythm Lines 1, 2 and 3 on page 42.

RHYTHM PATTERNS
Quarter Notes and Quarter Rests

1. Clap and **SAY** each line. 2. Clap and **THINK** each line. 3. Select a note and **PLAY** each line.

REST TEST

To keep your place in the music, look at each note and rest as you play.

DUO DE ESPAÑA
SPANISH DUET

Ed Sueta

Play Premier Technique Lines 5 and 6 on page 44.

18

TIME SIGNATURE

3 = 3 beats in a measure
4 = quarter note receives 1 beat

DOTTED HALF NOTE

A dotted half note receives 3 beats in ¾ and 4/4 time. The dot adds half the value of the note.

SLUR

A slur is a curved line that connects notes of different pitches. Tongue the first note only.

COUNTING THREE

DOWN IN THE VALLEY

Kentucky Mountain Song

WALTZ FOR TWO

Ed Sueta

Keep your air steady and even during all slurs and ties.

MARCH OF THE VICTORS

Football Song

1.

2.

Play Premier Technique Lines 7 and 8 on page 44.

Play Premier Rhythm Lines 6 and 7 on page 42.

EIGHTH NOTE RHYTHM PATTERNS

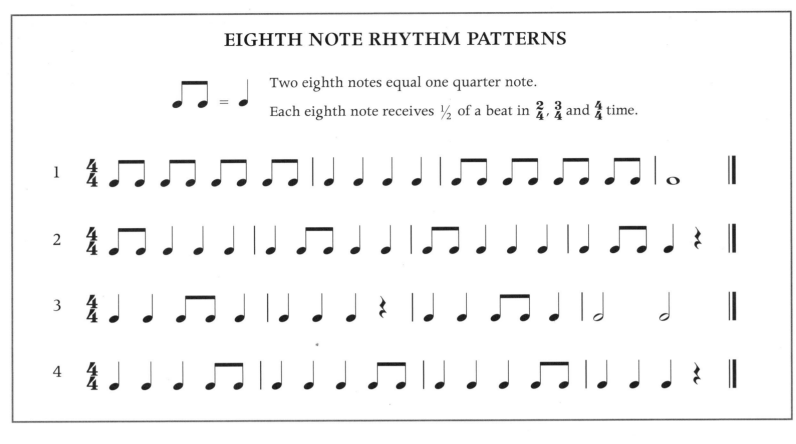

Two eighth notes equal one quarter note.

Each eighth note receives ½ of a beat in 2/4, 3/4 and 4/4 time.

EIGHTH NOTE PATTERNS

Line 56 is not in unison.

MEXICAN FIESTA!

Sierra Madre Region

Moderato

SQUARE DANCE

Ed Sueta

Lively

Play Premier Technique Lines 9 and 10 on page 44.

DYNAMICS

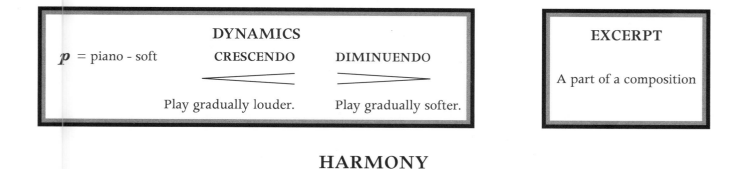

p = piano - soft **CRESCENDO** **DIMINUENDO**

Play gradually louder. Play gradually softer.

EXCERPT

A part of a composition

HARMONY

SEA SONG

English Shanty

DANCE OF THE REED FLUTES
EXCERPT FROM THE NUTCRACKER SUITE

Peter Ilyich Tchaikovsky
(1840-1893)

Quick breaths are necessary. As you breathe in, do not lift your shoulders.

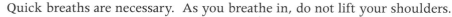

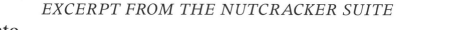

Play Premier Rhythm Lines 8, 9 and 10 on page 42.

22

ACCIDENTAL
An accidental is a sharp, flat or natural which is not in the key signature. It lasts for 1 measure.

TEMPO
ANDANTE
Moderately slow
ALLEGRO
Fast and lively

FERMATA
Hold the note a little longer.
RITARD
Gradually slower

SLOW AND ACCURATE

LIL LIZA JANE
American Folk Tune

CARIBBEAN CHA CHA
Ed Sueta

accidental   The natural sign (♮) cancels the flat until the next measure.

WAYFARING STRANGER
Folk Ballad

THEME FROM MIDSUMMER NIGHT'S DREAM
Felix Mendelssohn
(1809-1847)

Play Premier Rhythm Lines 11 and 12 on page 43.

RANGE PATROL

Line 67 is not in unison.

CLEAR SOUNDS

Line 68 is not in unison.

IT'S ME O LORD

Spiritual

EIGHTH RESTS

PIZZA POLKA

Ed Sueta

A SHADE OF BLUE

Ed Sueta

Play Premier Rhythm Lines 13 and 14 on page 43.

Play Premier Technique Lines 11 and 12 on page 45.

MARCH TO THE DRY GULCH

25

Complete this Rest Test and then play your composition.

Play Premier Rhythm Lines 15 and 16 on page 43.

26

WHEN THE SAINTS GO MARCHING IN

Moderato

American

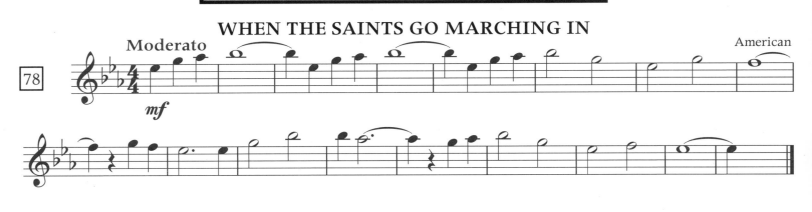

78

mf

MISS MACIE

Lively

Ed Sueta

79

mf

FAIS DO DO

Andante

French Canadian Lullaby

Fine

80

mp legato

mf

D.C. al Fine

PETITE POLKA

Con spirito

Ed Sueta

81

mf

1.

2.

CINDY IN TWO KEYS

Moderato

American Pioneer Song

82

mp

mf

CHI CHI CHA CHA

D.S. - **Dal Segno al Coda** - Go back to the sign (𝄋) and play to the Coda (⊕).

LAKE STATION MARCH

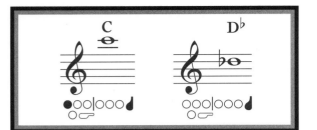

DAL SEGNO AL FINE (D.S. AL FINE)

Go back to the sign (𝄋) and play to the *Fine*.

LONG TONES

83 Line 83 is not in unison.

RANGE CONTROL

84 Line 84 is not in unison.

INDIAN CHANT

Native American

85 Slowly
mf

OH SUSANNAH

Stephen Foster
(1826-1864)

86 Lively
mf

Fine *f*

D.S. al Fine *mf*

JULIE'S BLUES

Ed Sueta

87 Moderato D♭
mf

UP ON THE HOUSE TOP

Traditional Christmas Song

88 Moderato
mf

Play Premier Technique Lines 13 and 14 on page 45.

TEMPO

ALLEGRETTO

Moderately fast

CLARINETS FLYING HIGH

SECOND FLIGHT

SAFE LANDING

THIRD FLIGHT

STEADY DOES IT

1. Tongue all notes. 2. Slur as marked.

SMOOTH CONNECTIONS

PORTUGUESE WALTZ

Algarve Region

FOR FLUTES

When this line becomes easy to play, increase your speed.

AIR CONTROL

Write in seconds

97

How many seconds can you hold each note?

SMOOTH AND EVEN

98

ALPINE MOUNTAIN SONG

Not too fast

Swiss Folk Song

99

mf

WINTER GOOD-BYE

German Melody

Andante

100A

mf legato

Andante

100B

mf legato

p

p

FOR FLUTES

101

1. Tongue all notes *mf*. 2. Slur as marked *mp*.

Play Premier Technique Lines 15 and 16 on page 45.

Quarter note tied to an eighth note

ALL TIED UP

102

JINGLE BELLS

James S. Pierpont
(1822-1893)

103 Moderato

mf

THEME FROM THE NINTH SYMPHONY

Ludwig van Beethoven
(1770-1827)

104 Moderato

mf

Tie only on the *D.S.*

p

Fine

D.S. al Fine

mf

SOURWOOD MOUNTAIN

Appalachian Folk Song

105 Lively

mf

Play Premier Technique Lines 17 and 18 on page 45.

A dotted quarter note receives 1½ beats in 2/4, 3/4 and 4/4 time.

Dotted quarter - eighth note

COUNTING DOTS

TWO SPIRITUALS

Andante   STEAL AWAY

Moderato   GIVE ME THAT OLD TIME RELIGION

TYROLEAN DANCE

Allegro   Austrian Folk Dance

THE OVERLANDER

Lively   *THE QUEENSLAND DROVER**   Australian Folk Song

* A drover is an Australian cowboy.

How fast can you say the notes and rests?

Fill in the number of beats

Play Premier Rhythm Lines 17 and 18 on page 43.

TYRANNOSAURUS REX STOMP

Jim Engebretson

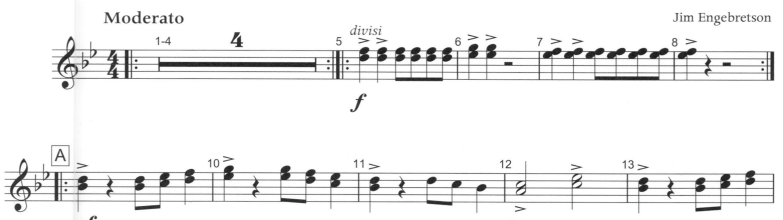

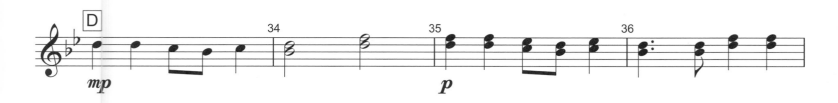

34

SMOOTH AND ACCURATE

B♭ SCALE

Also play the B♭ scale as half notes.

MARINES HYMN

March Tempo

American
Fine

mf

D.C. al Fine

UN CANADIEN ERRANT

Andante

Canadian Folk Song

mp

CHORALE

Moderato

Franz Joseph Haydn
(1732-1809)

1.

2.

mf

MINUET

Allegretto

Michel Corrette
(1712-1768)

mf

TWO WAYS - SAME SOUND

ALMA MATER

College Song

OLD BRASS WAGON

American Pioneer Song

Eᵇ SCALE

Also play the Eᵇ scale as half notes.

KUM BA YAH

Spiritual

Play Premier Rhythm Lines 19 and 20 on page 43.

Play Premier Technique Lines 19 and 20 on page 45.

36

AMERICA

Samuel Francis Smith
(1808-1895)

CLEAR SOUNDS

EXCERPT FROM LA TRAVIATA - ACT III

Giuseppe Verdi
(1813-1901)

ROCKIN' ALONG

Ed Sueta

COMMODORE MARCH

FLUTE SOLO

THEME BY CHOPIN

Frederic Chopin
(1810-1849)

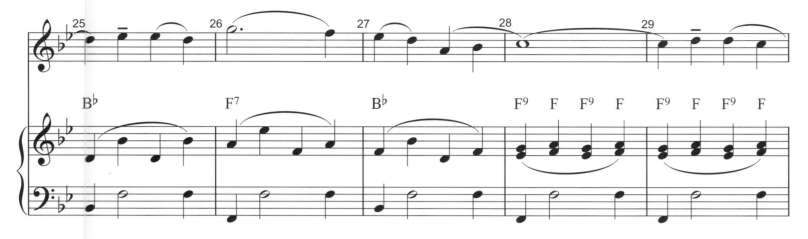

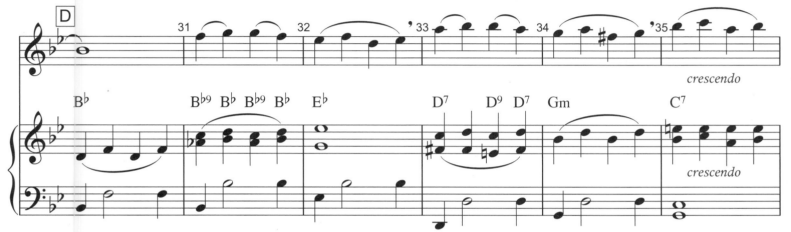

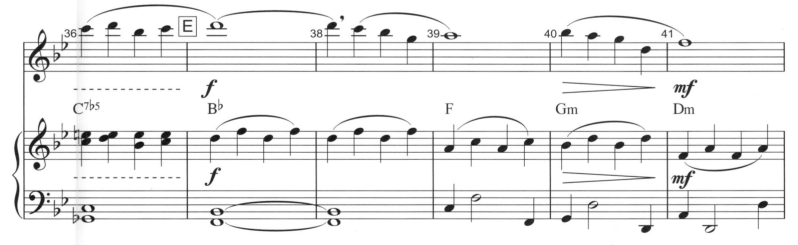

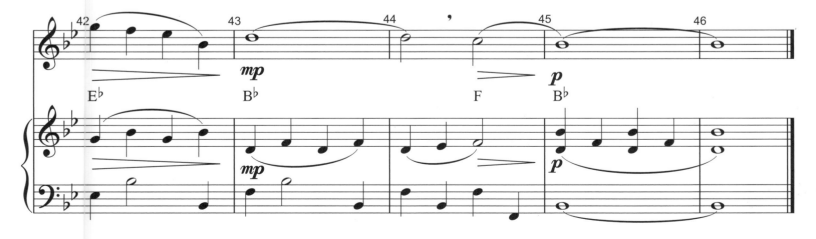

ALPINE OVERTURE

Quincy Hilliard

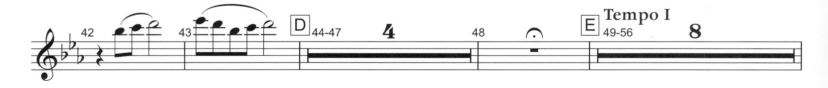

MAJOR SCALES AND ARPEGGIOS

42

PREMIER RHYTHMS

1. Clap and **SAY** each line.
2. Clap and **THINK** each line.
3. **PLAY** each line on any of the notes you have learned.
4. After a line becomes easy, **INCREASE** your speed.

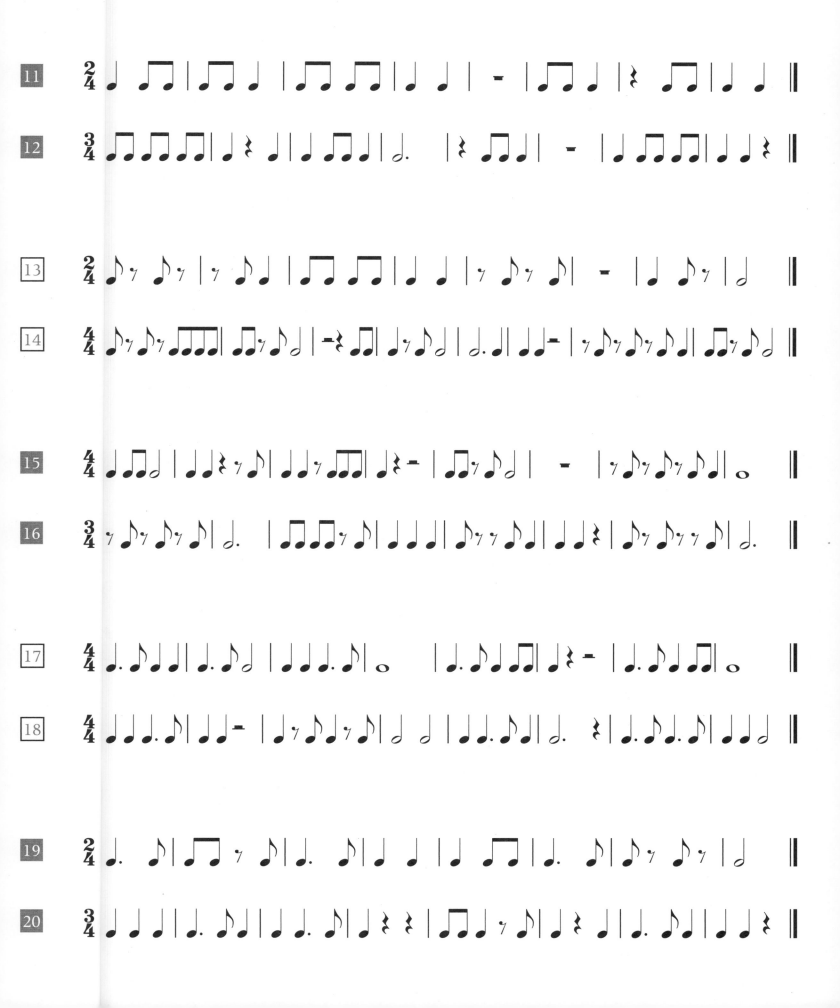

PREMIER TECHNIQUE

1. **PLAY** each line several times.
2. Always be **ACCURATE**.
3. Always keep your fingers **CLOSE** to the keys.
4. When a line becomes easy, **INCREASE** your speed.

1. Tongue all notes. 2. Slur as marked.

11

Articulations:

12 1. Tongue all notes. 2. Slur as marked.

13

14

15 1. Tongue all notes. 2. Slur as marked.

16 1. Tongue all notes. 2. Slur as marked.

17

18 1. Tongue all notes. 2. Slur as marked.

19

20

THE HISTORY OF THE FLUTE

The flute is a woodwind instrument. Most woodwind instruments were originally made of wood. Today, flutes are different from most other woodwind instruments because they are made of metal. The flute is also different from the other woodwind instruments because the flute does not have a reed.

The flute is the highest pitched woodwind instrument with the exception of the piccolo. The piccolo is a small half-size wooden or metal version of the flute and is pitched one octave higher than the flute. The piccolo gets its name from the Italian *flauto piccolo* or "little flute." The flute and piccolo have the same fingerings.

The flute is one of the oldest instruments and dates back nearly 40,000 years. Cave men made a primitive form of the flute by carving holes in the bones of animals. Later, wooden flutes were found in many parts of the world including India, China and Japan. These early flutes were held directly in front of the player. Etruscan art work from 200 B.C. pictured flutes which were held to the side. This type of flute is called a transverse flute. Transverse flutes were not seen in Europe until 1100 A.D.

Many attempts were made to improve the pitch and tone quality of the flute. The most important changes were made by a German flutist and instrument maker named Theobald Boehm. Boehm was the first person to make flutes of metal. From 1832 to 1850, he developed a mechanical system of keys, levers and pads which allowed flutists to play a wider range of notes. Today, different versions of the Boehm key system are used for all the woodwind instruments with the exception of the bassoon.

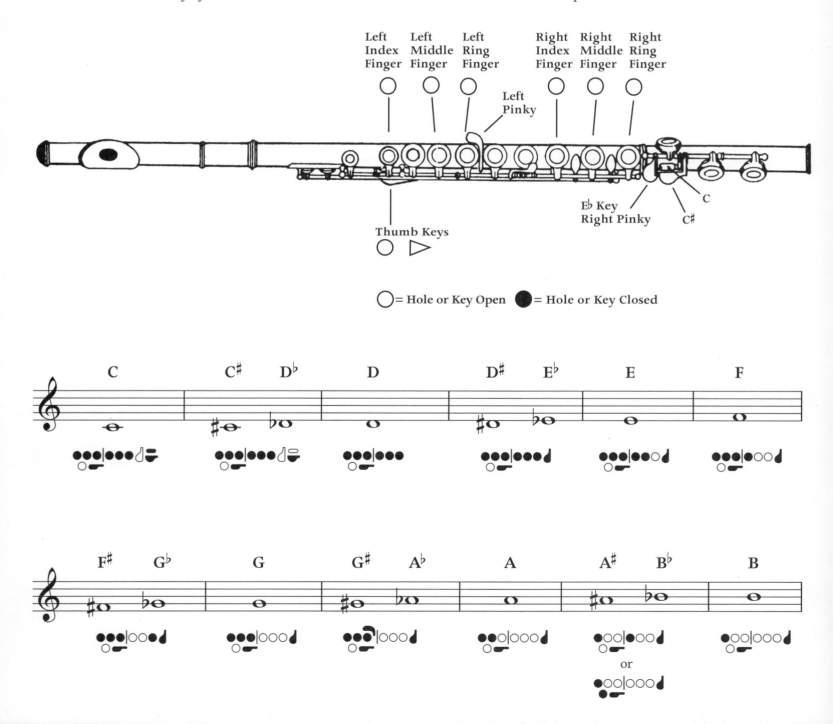

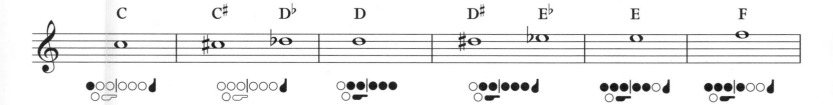

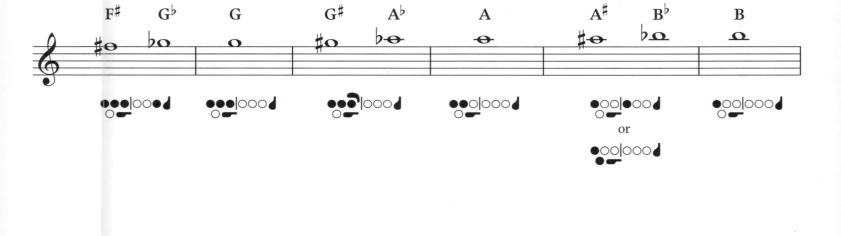

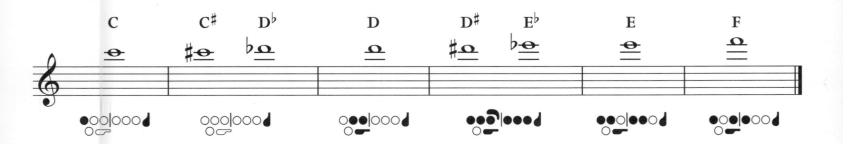

MUSIC DICTIONARY

MUSICAL SYMBOLS

	Accent	Emphasis is given to a note by playing it a little louder
	Accidental	A sharp (♯), flat (♭), or natural (♮) not indicated in the key signature
	Breath Mark	A place to take a breath
	Coda	Ending section of a composition
C	Common Time	Same as $\frac{4}{4}$ time
	Crescendo	Gradually louder
	Diminuendo	Gradually softer
V	Dominant Chord	A chord built on the fifth note of the scale
	Fermata	Hold the note or rest a little longer
♭	Flat	Lowers the pitch of a note one half step
♮	Natural	Cancels a sharp or flat until the next bar line
	One measure repeat	Repeat the previous measure
	Two measure repeat	Repeat the previous two measures
	Repeat Sign	Play the music again from the beginning
♯	Sharp	Raises the pitch of a note one half step
	Slur	A curved line that connects notes of different pitches
	Staccato	Separated; detached
IV	Subdominant Chord	A chord built on the fourth note of the scale
	Tenuto	Hold the note for its full value
	Tie	A curved line that connects notes of the same pitch
I	Tonic Chord	A chord built on the first note of the scale

MUSICAL TERMS

Accelerando (Accel.)	Gradually faster
A Tempo	Resume the original speed
Cantabile	Singing style
Da Capo al Fine	Go back to the beginning and play to the *Fine*
Dal Segno al Coda	Go back to the sign (𝄋) and play to the *Coda*
Dal Segno al Fine	Go back to the sign (𝄋) and play to the *Fine*
Divisi	Some players play the upper notes while other players play the lower notes
Duet	A composition with parts for two players
Espressivo	With expression
Excerpt	A part of a composition
Key signature	The sharp(s) or flat(s) placed to the right of a clef on a staff which indicate(s) which notes are to be sharped or flatted
Legato	Smoothly; play smoothly with no separation between the notes
Phrase	A musical sentence
Pick-up note(s)	Note(s) before the first complete measure of a song
Rallentando (Rall.)	Gradually slower
Ritardando (Rit.)	Gradually slower
Round	Playing the same music but beginning at different times
Simile	The same; continue in the same manner
Solo	One person plays
Tacet	Silent
Theme	The main melody in a musical composition
Unison	All players play the same pitch

DYNAMICS (Loud and Soft) MARKINGS

pp	*pianissimo*	Very soft
p	*piano*	Soft
mp	*mezzo piano*	Moderately soft
mf	*mezzo forte*	Moderately loud
f	*forte*	Loud
ff	*fortissimo*	Very loud

TEMPO (Speed) MARKINGS

Adagio	Slow
Allegretto	Moderately fast
Allegro	Fast and lively
Andante	Moderately slow
Con Spirito	With spirit
Largo	Very slow; flowing
Maestoso	Majestically; stately
Moderato	Moderate speed
Presto	Very fast; faster than Allegro
Vivace	Lively; briskly